I Like Cars

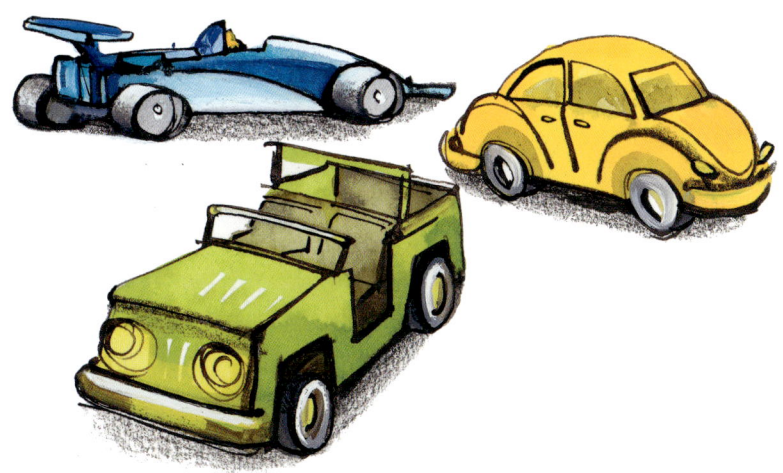

Claire Llewellyn
Illustrated by Helen van Vliet

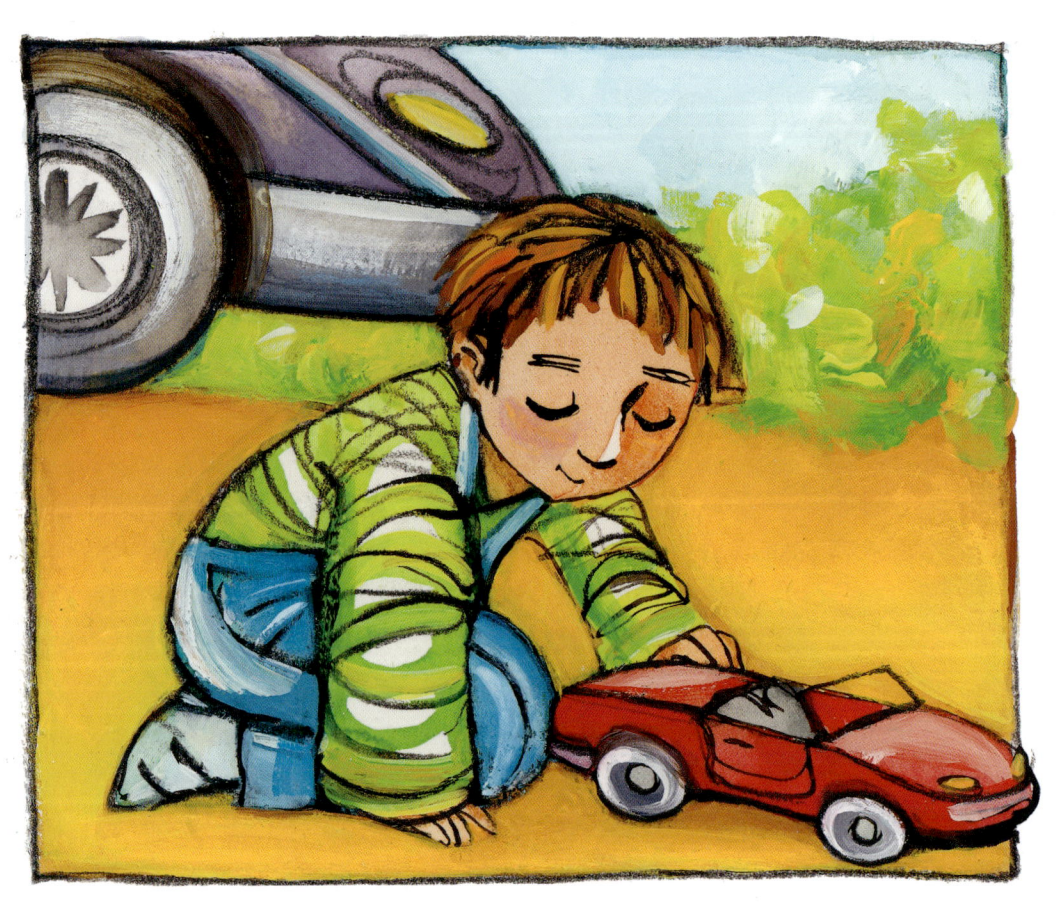

I like the red car.

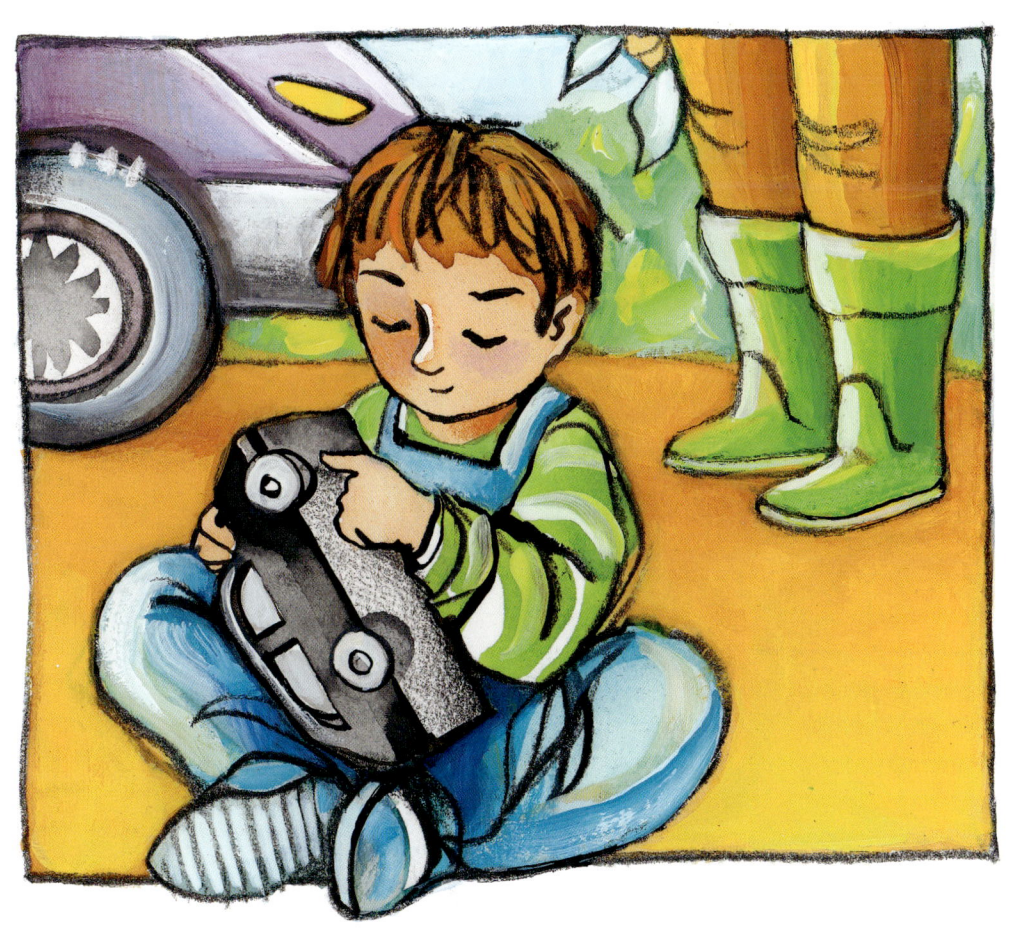

I like the black car.

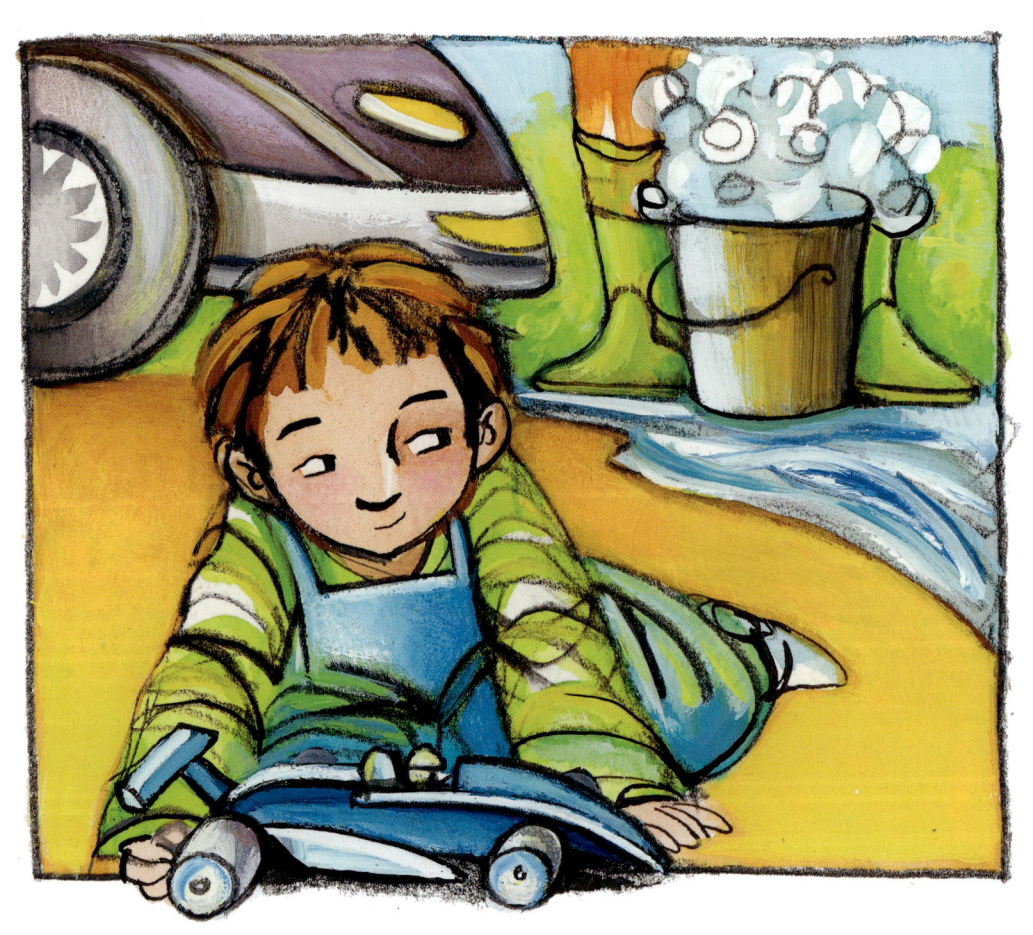

I like the blue car.

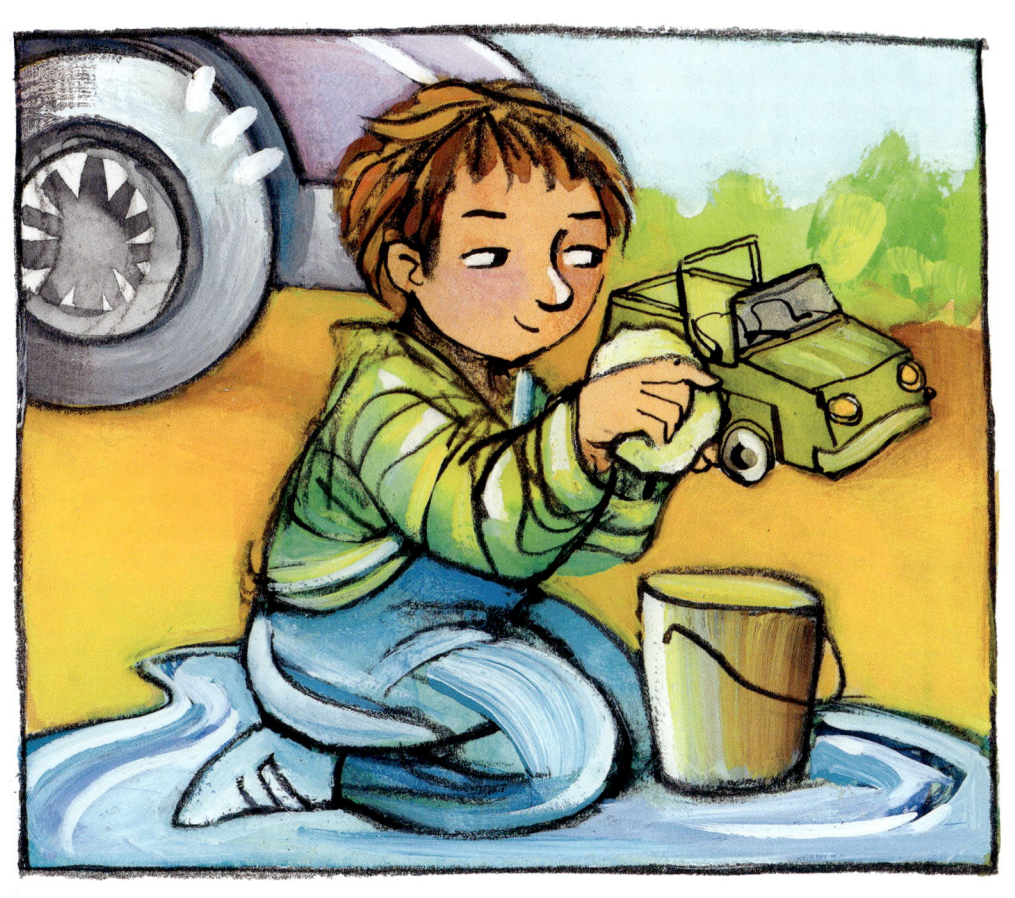

I like the green car.

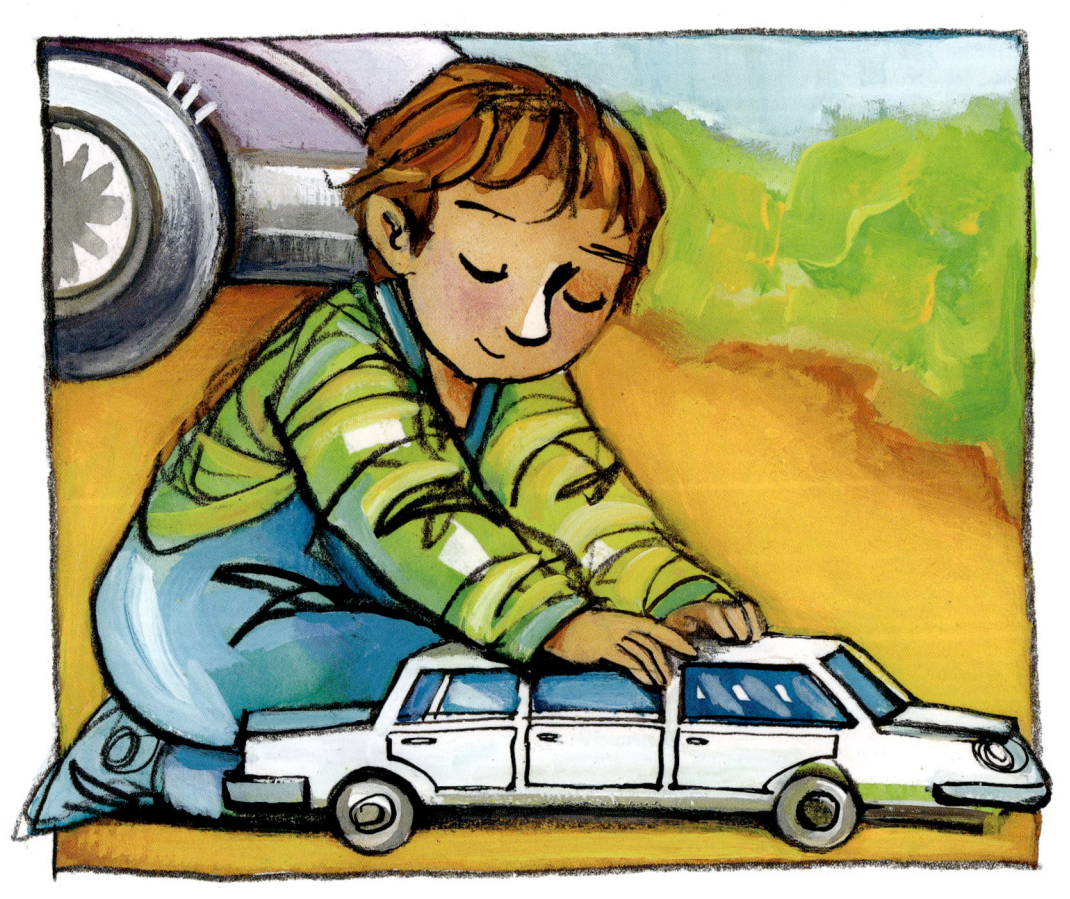

I like the white car.

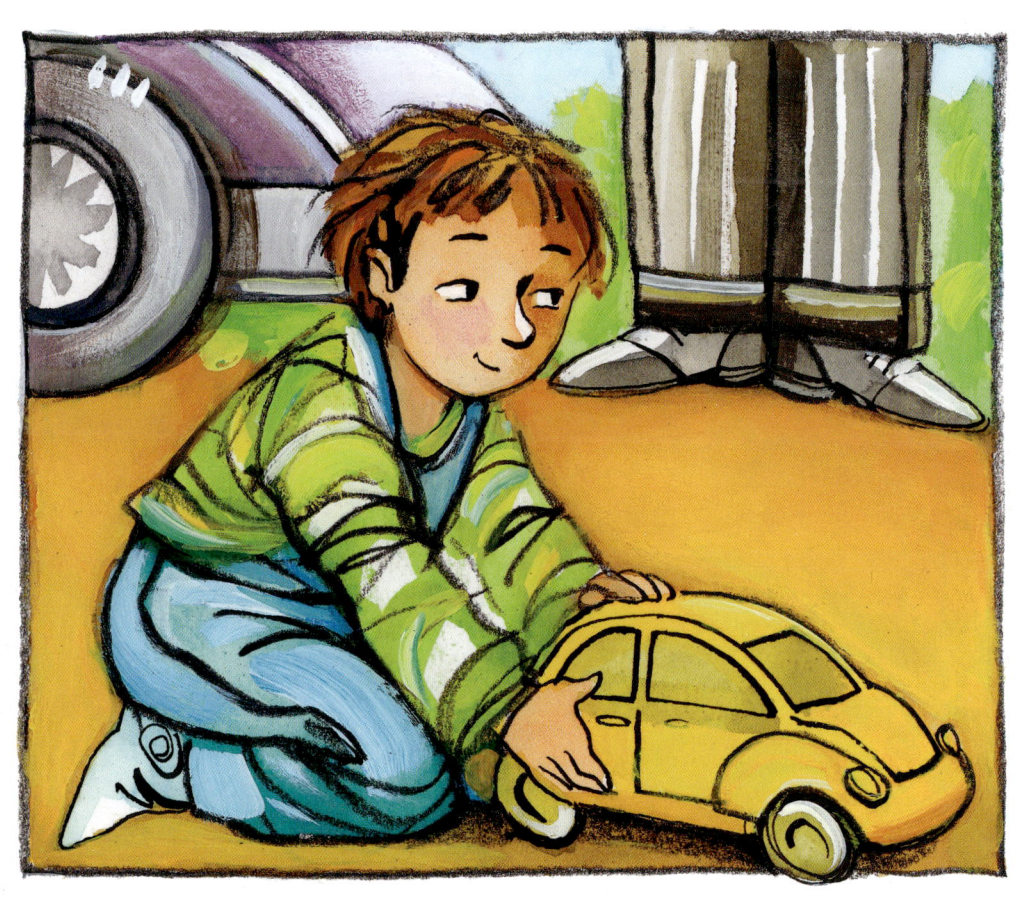

I like the yellow car.

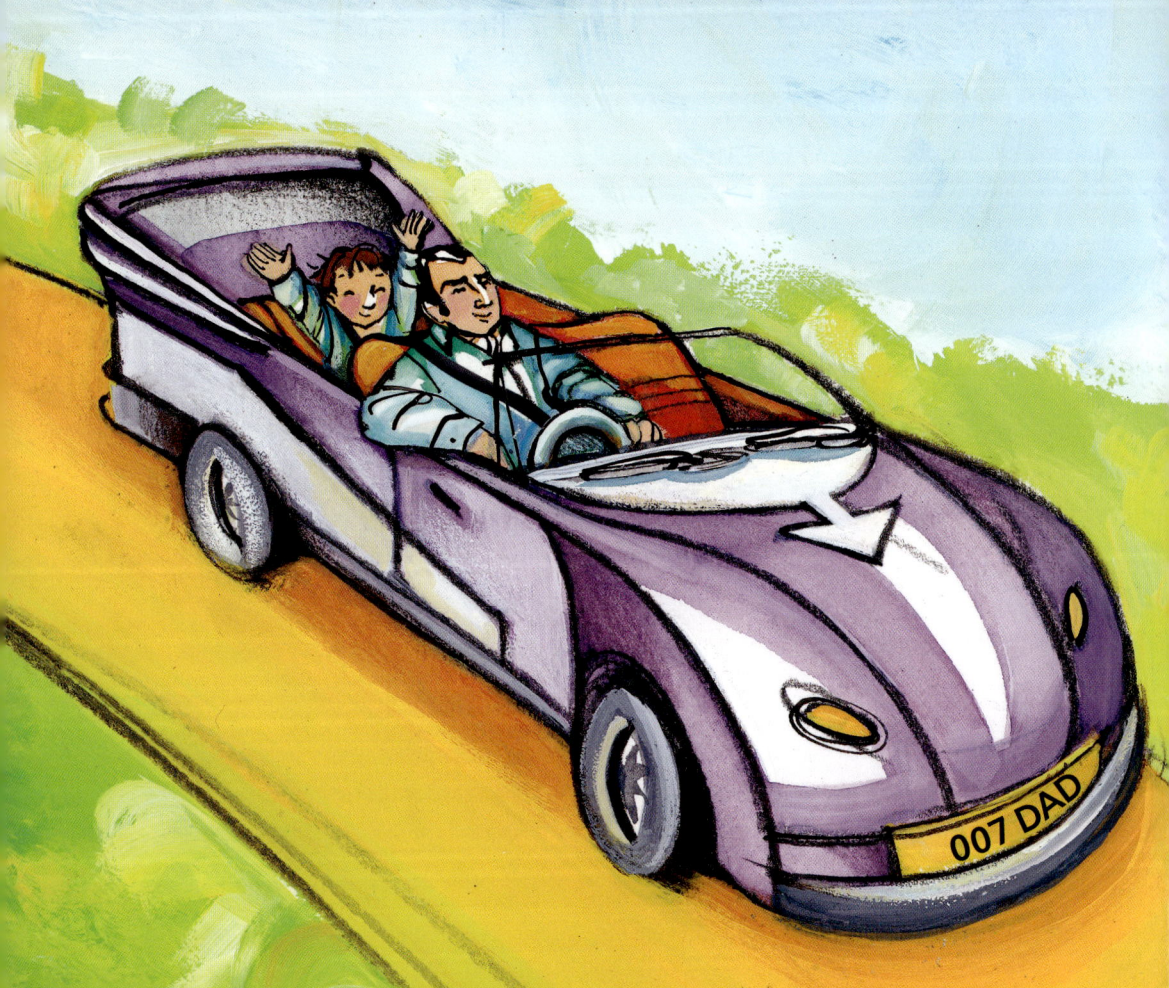

But I love my dad's car!